MISSION
LISBON

www.ScavengerHuntAdventures.com

Creator: Catherine Aragon • Cover Designer: Nada Orlić • Editor: Uma Sahaja

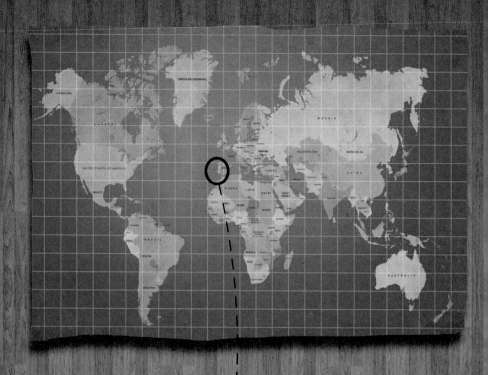

ATLANTIC
OCEAN

PORTUGAL

SINTRA
LISBON

SPAIN

ATLANTIC
OCEAN

CONTENTS

After finishing a mission, write the number of points earned & check the box.

At the end, write the total number of points here:

ATTENTION: FUTURE SPECIAL AGENTS <u>YOU</u>

AND CASE OFFICERS <u>GROWNUPS</u>

CONGRATULATIONS! THE SIA (SECRET INTERNATIONAL AGENCY) HAS SELECTED YOU AS A CANDIDATE TO BECOME A SPECIAL AGENT. The SIA carries out secret missions, collecting intelligence around the globe. ("Intelligence" is spy-speak for "information.") We need new agents. Many want to join, but few have what it takes.

DO YOU HAVE WHAT IT TAKES TO JOIN THE MOST ELITE SPY AGENCY IN THE WORLD? You must complete a series of missions in Portugal. Similar to a scavenger hunt (only better), these missions require you to complete challenging investigations and collect valuable intel (short for "intelligence"). For each mission, you'll earn points towards becoming a special agent.

YOUR ASSIGNMENT: TRAVEL TO PORTUGAL WITH YOUR TEAM, LED BY YOUR CASE OFFICER. (A case officer accompanies agents on missions. Your case officer is your parent or other trusted adult.)

1. TO "WIN" THE HUNT AND BECOME AN AGENT YOU MUST:
- If you visit Lisbon only: earn 150 points
- If you visit Sintra only: earn 100 points
- If you visit Lisbon *and* Sintra: earn 200 points
- No need to complete all missions to earn enough points or complete them in any set order.

2. YOU MUST ALSO BREAK THE CODE ON P.50.
- Tip: Lookout for clue labels like this........ | CLUE 1 |

3. BE SURE TO TAKE A LOOK AT:
- the mission list and scorecard on p.1
- Anytime Missions (p.42) & Anytime Missions Bonus (p.49) early so you don't miss out on points
- each mission's pages before starting a mission

4. BRING A PEN/PENCIL AND CAMERA/PHONE CAMERA.

BONUS MISSION

Want more Lisbon fun? Case officers, visit
ScavengerHuntAdventures.Com/Bonus

- download a free Lisbon hunt
- you can use it with this book

MISSION RULES

- Be kind and respectful to team members.

- Your case officer (your parent or other trusted adult) has the final decision regarding point awards.

- Your case officer serves as the official "scorekeeper."

- Your case officer has the final decision on what missions will be attempted. (Don't worry, you can still earn enough points & break the code to "win" without completing all the missions.)

- Always be on alert. You never know when a chance to earn points lies just around the corner.

TO CONCEAL THEIR REAL IDENTITIES, SPECIAL AGENTS ALWAYS USE CODE NAMES. FOR EXAMPLE, JAMES BOND'S CODE NAME IS 007. THINK OF YOUR OWN CODE NAME TO USE DURING YOUR MISSION IN PORTUGAL.

SIGN YOUR CODE NAME BELOW:

....

PHOTO CONTEST

Want a chance at bragging rights and an Amazon giftcard?

Take a clever pic of your MISSION book in Portugal (or back at home).

Then, case officers, go to our website & enter our photo contest:

ScavengerHuntAdventures.Com/Contest

"I'm Entering Today!"

JERONIMOS MONASTERY

SPECIAL AGENTS NEED TO HAVE SHARP EYES FOR DETAILS. THE BEST AGENTS HAVE THEIR EYES PEELED FOR THE SMALLEST CLUE & IMPORTANT INFO THAT OTHERS OFTEN MISS. TIME TO PUT YOUR SKILLS TO THE TEST.

The monks* who called this place home hundreds of years ago lived according to the life lessons of St. Jerome (Jeronimos = of St. Jerome). According to legend, Jerome became friends with an injured lion after he managed to remove a thorn stuck deep in the lion's paw. While we don't recommend getting too close to lions, this story does show the importance of helping others and of friendship.

*monks give up "regular" life for a very simple life at a monastery; monks devote their lives to God and helping others

SOUTH PORTAL

ST. JEROME

SOUTH PORTAL (OUTSIDE)

☐ FIND THE SOUTH PORTAL (DOORWAY). **2** POINTS

☐ LOCATE ST. JEROME (WITH HIS LION). **1** POINT

☐ FIND ST. MARY. **1** POINT

Sailors would pray to St. Mary before setting off from Lisbon on dangerous sea voyages.

ST. MARY

☐ LOCATE PRINCE HENRY. **1** POINT

He stands between two wooden doors holding a sword. Thanks to his money and careful planning, he set Portugal up to be super-successful in the Age of Exploration. Portugal created trade routes to Africa, Asia, and eventually the Americas. Then, the race was on among the kingdoms of Europe (mainly Portugal, Spain, England, France, the Netherlands) to snatch up as much as they could from these lands: spices, sugar, other crops; gold, gems, and, tragically, slaves.

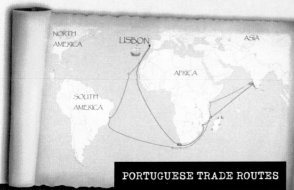

PORTUGUESE TRADE ROUTES

PRINCE HENRY

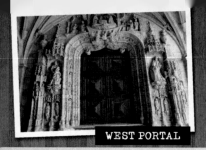

WEST PORTAL

WEST PORTAL (OUTSIDE)

☐ **LOCATE THE WEST PORTAL (DOORWAY).** **2 POINTS**

Hint: Outside the South Portal, face the door. Go to your left, then under the arch just before the lawn.

☐ **TRACK DOWN KING MANUEL WITH ST. JEROME.** **1 POINT**

☐ **BONUS: FIND ST. JEROME'S LION BEHIND HIM.** **1 POINT**

Manuel had this place built for the monks and to honor St. Mary, St. Jerome, and Prince Henry. He also wanted a final resting place for Portugal's royal family.

And, judging by the looks of this place, he probably just wanted to show off a bit. Track down his symbols everywhere, and get ready to earn points!

☐ **FIND CROSSES LIKE THIS. 1 PT EACH, 5 PTS MAX** **1 POINT EACH**

Cross of the Military Order of Christ

(Manuel was one of the group's leaders.)

Don't forget the "Anytime Missions" sphere on p.47. You'll find loads here.

my notes:

....

....

....

INSIDE

Did you arrive to Portugal in a plane (or maybe by crossing the Spanish border in a car/ train)? Back when this place was built, for long-distance travel, ships were the way to go. And the Portuguese had totally mastered how to sail long distances, thanks in part to the speedy caravel.

☐ **FIND THIS CARAVEL (A TYPE OF SHIP).** **2** POINTS

Hint: Look for the shoes above.

☐ **THIS IS THE TOMB OF WHICH EXPLORER?** **1** POINT

Hint: Find a sign nearby for the answer.

Ever help your parents cook? If you could time-travel back to the days of this explorer, the spices in your kitchen (pepper, cinnamon, nutmeg, etc.) could make you rich! Spices made (sometimes rotten) food taste better and were used as medicine. Hauling spices all the way from where they grew in Asia to Western Europe was tricky. It took too much time and money. A better way would be a sea route around Africa. So, Portugal's explorers tried for years to get to India (the "Spice Capital") this way. After sailing from Lisbon in 1497, with ships like the caravel you found, this explorer finally did it. **Jackpot.**

SPICE MERCHANT

PEPPER HARVEST - INDIA

THE EXPLORER

THE SYMBOLS

THE POET

☐ **FIND THESE SYMBOLS OF PORTUGAL'S GREAT POET.** **2 POINTS**

It's a feather, harp, and book. The poet above isn't winking. Sadly, he lost an eye while fighting in the military. His poem, about the explorer from the earlier page, goes something like this:

"What wars they waged, what seas, what dangers passed, what glorious empire crowned their toils at last!" (toils = hard work)

☐ **WRITE THE POET'S LAST NAME BELOW.** **1 POINT**
Hint: A nearby sign has his name.

__ __ __ __ __ __

CLUE 1   CLUE 2

Be sure the right letters are on the **darker lines**. You'll use this info in "Break the Code" on p.50.

CLOISTER (COURTYARD) ················

In the cloister locate:

☐ **PORTUGUESE SHIP** **2 POINTS**

☐ **THREE CREATURES BELOW** **2 POINTS EACH**
More on the next page.

my notes:

☐ EXAMINE THE DIFFERENT CREATURE STATUES/ CREATURE SCULPTURES IN THE COURTYARD. CHOOSE YOUR TWO FAVORITES, AND TAKE A PIC OF THEM.

1
POINT

SPECIAL AGENTS MUST THINK FAST ON THEIR FEET. TIME TO TEST YOUR SKILLS.

Come up with a unique story about each of the two creatures in your pics. Each of your two stories must include this info about the creature:

•Their Name   •Their Age   •Their Hobbies
•Why they're important to the monastery

If you need ideas, think about the story of St. Jerome and the lion. Then, tell each of these two stories to your team. Your team will choose which one of your two stories is the better!

☐ FOUR POINTS FOR YOUR TWO UNIQUE STORIES.

4
POINTS

my notes:

THE BEST AGENTS HAVE EXCELLENT IMAGE ANALYSIS SKILLS.

Here, that basically means looking very carefully at a picture. Track down this painting of St. Jerome and his lion in the "refectory" (the monks' dining room).

☐ **FIND 3 THINGS MISSING IN THIS PAINTING COMPARED TO THE ORIGINAL IN THE DINING ROOM.**

3 POINTS

Time for some translating into Portuguese. Together with your case officer, ask a Portuguese person for help with this or look it up together online.

☐ **WRITE THE WORD "LION" IN PORTUGUESE BELOW.**
  *BE SURE TO USE THE WORD FOR A <u>MALE</u> LION.

1 POINT

CLUE 3   CLUE 4

Be sure the right letters are on the **darker lines.** You'll use this info in "Break the Code" on p.50.

BELÉM TOWER

("Beh-leyn"; Belém = Bethlehem)

AS A SPECIAL AGENT, YOU MUST "HIDE IN PLAIN SIGHT" – THAT MEANS ACTING LIKE A REGULAR TOURIST – BY EXPLORING THIS TOWER.

During the Age of Exploration (p.5), explorers sailed off from this very spot. Their destination: the New World or Asia. Their main goal: return with ships full of riches (spices, gold, etc.).

Outside, just before the bridge leading to the tower, track down Belém Tower model (above). Compare it to the actual tower in front of you.

☐ **ON A SCALE OF 1 TO 5 STARS, IN YOUR OPINION, ASIDE FROM THE COLOR, HOW ACCURATE IS THIS MODEL VS. THE ORIGINAL?**

1 POINT

> If your team doesn't plan on actually going inside the tower, you can still earn points by closely examining the tower's outside.

This place may look like a fancy castle, but it served as a military fortress, ready to protect Portugal's capital from any enemy ships that dared sail into the harbor. Time to locate these reminders of the tower's time as a fortress:

☐ AN ARROW SLIT (ABOVE, RIGHT) **1** POINT

☐ CANNONS (1 POINT EACH, 5 POINTS MAX) **1** POINT EACH

King Manuel wanted you to know exactly who had this place built - he did! Track down his symbols everywhere.

☐ FIND CROSSES LIKE THIS. (10 PTS MAX) **1** POINT EACH

Cross of the Military Order of Christ (Manuel was one of the group's leaders.)

☐ MAKE YOUR WAY TO THE LOWER TERRACE THAT FACES THE RIVER. **2** POINTS

☐ HERE, LOCATE THE STATUE OF MOTHER & CHILD
(MARY & JESUS).

2 POINTS

☐ WHAT FRUIT DOES MARY HOLD?

1 POINT

From the statue, look up at the tower and you can
see a lovely porch/balcony on the next level up.

☐ ONCE BACK INSIDE, TRACK DOWN THIS BALCONY
(OR ANOTHER) AND LOOK OUT OVER THE RIVER.

1 POINT

From here, tower guests could relax and watch
ships sail on the river, the Tejo (Tagus in
English). Any ships out on the Tejo today?

☐ MAKE YOUR WAY UP TO THE TOP LEVEL TERRACE.

2 POINTS

☐ SPOT PORTUGAL'S FLAG
(FLYING HERE OR FROM
ANOTHER SPOT)

1 POINT

MONUMENT TO THE DISCOVERIES

ATTENTION TO DETAIL: THIS IS A KEY SKILL FOR A SPECIAL AGENT. TIME TO PUT YOUR SKILLS TO THE TEST BY UNCOVERING THE SMALLEST OF CLUES.

☐ THE EASY PART FIRST: FIND THE MAP ABOVE. **1** POINT

☐ LOCATE THE THREE PARTS OF PORTUGAL. **2** POINTS

Mainland Portugal, the Açores (islands) and Madeira (islands)

1427
AÇORES

MADEIRA

☐ TRACK DOWN A PORTUGUESE SHIP LIKE THE ONE ABOVE. (2 POINTS EACH, 10 POINTS MAX)

2 POINTS EACH

☐ FIND A SEA GOD HOLDING A TRIDENT (SIMILAR TO THIS ONE).

2 POINTS

☐ LOCATE YOUR HOME ON THE MAP.

2 POINTS

☐ WHAT DOES PRINCE HENRY HOLD IN HIS HAND IN THE MONUMENT TO THE DISCOVERIES?

2 POINTS

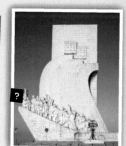

Prince Henry (p.5) leads the crew on this monument which honors the Age of Exploration.

my notes:

PRAÇA DO COMÉRCIO

("Pra-sa do Koe-mayr-see-oh") *(Commerce Square)*

Hunt down the above statue. We've altered the image on the right by removing an animal .

☐ **WRITE THE NAME OF THE MISSING ANIMAL.** **2 POINTS**

CLUE 6   CLUE 7

Be sure the right letters are on the **darker lines**. You'll use this info in "Break the Code" on p.50.

Here stands history's (probably) only king who **lived in tents** instead of palaces: King José. In **1755**, **disaster** struck Lisbon - a terrible **earthquake**... followed by a **tsunami**. Much of Lisbon crumbled. (Most buildings back then weren't quake-proof.) All this made

King José develop **"claustrophobia"** (a fear of closed-in spaces). So for the rest of his reign, he lived and worked in **fancy tents**.

☐ IN THE SAME STATUE, LOCATE THIS MAN. **1** POINT

(Just like in the painting, a cross rests around his neck.)

Following the disaster of 1755, this man (the Marques do Pombal) led the way to rebuild Lisbon, making it safer in case another quake hit (so far, so good). Here, he wants you to admire the rebuilt port. (Quite a difference from the p.16 scene.)

☐ BONUS: IMAGE ANALYSIS TIME. FIND THE ANIMAL FROM P.16 IN THE PAINTING ABOVE. **1** POINT

☐ TRACK DOWN A NEARBY STREETLAMP TOPPED WITH LISBON'S SYMBOL (TWO RAVENS GUARDING A SHIP). **1** POINT

my notes:

....

....

....

STREET
LAMP'S TOP

Strolling this plaza around 80 years ago, you'd consider yourself extremely **lucky to be in Portugal**, and not somewhere else in Europe. Portugal didn't fight in **World War II** - they stayed **neutral**. Much of Europe, though, was in the midst of a **terrible war**. The evil Nazis wanted to control Europe. They hated many people, mainly those different than them, particularly Jewish people. (Nazis needed someone to blame for Germany's problems after the country lost World War I, even though Jewish people had nothing to do with it.)

Ever heard of **Curious George**? The creators of Curious George (Margret and H.A. Rey), like many other Jewish people, **fled to Lisbon** during World War II, where they were **safe**.

Back then, in this plaza stood a **post office** where those escaping would come, hoping to **get info** on lost friends/family. People also came to **make calls** to plan the last part of their **escape** out of Europe.

LONDON FOLLOWING BOMBING BY NAZIS

FREEDOM SHALL PREVAIL!

THE ALLIED POWERS (ABOVE) EVENTUALLY BEAT THE EVIL AXIS POWERS IN WWII

CURIOUS GEORGE

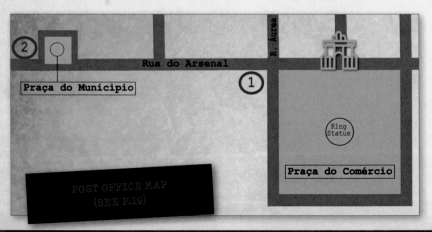

R. Áurea

② Praça do Municipio

Rua do Arsenal

①

King Statue

Praça do Comércio

POST OFFICE MAP
(SEE P.19)

CORREIO

TELEGRAFO   TELEFONE

☐ USE YOUR MAP-READING SKILLS TO TRACK DOWN THE SPOT OF THIS POST OFFICE.
("1" ON THE MAP ON P.18)

2 POINTS

You can still see faded marks from the words of the original sign imprinted on the outside wall.

☐ SUPER BONUS: FIND THE CURRENT POST OFFICE JUST DOWN THE STREET.
("2" ON THE MAP ON P.18)

3 POINTS

Hint: Look for the CTT sign.

☐ BUY A STAMP TO SEND A POSTCARD TO SOMEONE BACK HOME.

2 POINTS

As of 2020, a machine outside sells "selos", (stamps) if the office is closed. And if you can't accomplish this part of the mission now, then earn points by buying a postcard stamp before leaving Portugal.

Check out the plaza beside the post office to score points for the Anytime Missions p.45 (cobblestones) and p.47 (spheres).

SPECIAL AGENTS NEED A "COVER": A BELIEVABLE STORY THAT "COVERS" THEIR REAL MISSION. YOUR COVER: A TOURIST VISITING LISBON'S MAIN SQUARE & TOURIST STREET.

Head back to Praça do Comércio. Walk through the towering arch which leads from the plaza to a pedestrian street.

☐ **WRITE THE NAME OF THE STREET BELOW.**

2 POINTS

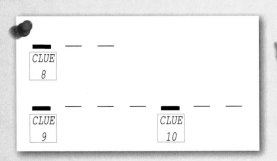

CLUE 8

CLUE 9   CLUE 10

Be sure the right letters are on the **darker lines.** You'll use this info in "Break the Code" on p.50.

Need help? Find a street sign on the arch for the answer.

Often, street performers entertain tourists on this street.

☐ 1 POINT FOR EACH STREET PERFORMER YOU SEE. (5 POINTS MAX)

1 POINT EACH

☐ IF YOU HAD TO WORK AS A STREET PERFORMER FOR A DAY, WHICH ONE WOULD YOU CHOOSE: A "STATUE", MUSICIAN, MIME, OR SINGER?

1 POINT

☐ IF YOU HAD TO ASSIGN YOUR CASE OFFICER(S) TO BE A STREET PERFORMER FOR A DAY, WHICH ONE WOULD YOU CHOOSE FOR THEM?

1 POINT

my notes:

ST. GEORGE'S CASTLE

Legend has it St. George, a knight who lived around 1,700 years ago, saved a town from an evil dragon. If George had lived in Lisbon, he would probably choose this castle — a spot with great views to keep a look out for any approaching enemies ... or dragons.

SPECIAL AGENTS MUST HAVE EXCELLENT MAP-READING SKILLS.

MAP

Castle entrance

Rua de Santa Cruz do Castelo

Rua do Recolhimento

archway

Rua do Chão da Feira

〰〰〰 = stone wall

2 POINTS

☐ LOCATE THIS SHRINE TO ST. GEORGE (IN YELLOW ON THE MAP).

At the beginning of the street that borders the castle entrance stands a small shrine to St. George — a figure of the saint behind glass.

KING AFONSO

← CASTLE

SIEGE OF LISBON, 1147

See the black dot on the map? According to our intel, you can find an "azulejo" of the castle at #20 Rua de Santa Cruz do Castelo, on the second level, between two windows.

☐ **LOCATE THIS AND ADD TO YOUR ANYTIME MISSIONS (P.44) SCORE.**

And if our intel is incorrect or if the azulejo is covered up, earn points by taking a team pic at the castle.

Venture inside the castle walls and find the statue below of Portugal's first king, Afonso I. Afonso led his troops to victory in the Siege of Lisbon against the Moors of North Africa, captured the castle, and became the first king of Portugal.

On his statue, find the large cross that divides the word "Portugal" into 4 groups.

☐ **WRITE THE 2 LETTERS IN THE TOP LEFT GROUP.**

2
POINTS

CLUE
5

Be sure the right letter is on the **darker line.** You'll use this info in "Break the Code" on p.50.

AFONSO STATUE

Peacocks roam around the castle grounds.

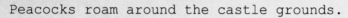

☐ 1 POINT FOR EACH PEACOCK SPOTTED
  (3 PTS MAX)

1
POINT

☐ 3 POINTS FOR EACH PEACOCK SPOTTED SHOWING
  OFF ITS FEATHERS (9 PTS MAX)

3
POINTS
EACH

☐ TRACK DOWN THE FLAG OF LISBON FLYING
  ABOVE THE CASTLE WALLS.

1
POINT

Lisbon's flag shows a ship guarded by two ravens
(black birds). See "Lisboa" on the banner at the
bottom of the flag? Lisboa = Lisbon. And, if you
want to sound like a true Portuguese, say Lisboa
like this: *"Leesh-boe-ah"*.

my notes:

CITY VIEWS

From St. George's Castle lookout points or other lookout points around the city, spot these:

☐ **25TH OF APRIL BRIDGE**  **1 POINT**
This bridge is named for "Freedom Day," April 25. Fifty years ago, Portugal had a super-strict, all-powerful government. You did what the government said, or else! The government wanted to keep tight control over the Portuguese people and parts of Africa (colonies). The Portuguese military and Portuguese people had had enough, so on April 25, 1974, they banded together to get rid of this awful government. Usually something like this is very violent, but in Portugal it happened pretty peacefully. Instead of using their guns, soldiers put red flowers (carnations) in them, giving this event the name the "Carnation Revolution."

☐ **BONUS: LATER, FIND A STREET SIGN WITH THIS NAME.** **3 POINTS** Over 1,000 streets and plazas have the name "25 de Abril." (Look for: Rua 25 de Abril, Avenida 25 Abril, or Praça 25 de Abril.)

☐ **VASCO DA GAMA BRIDGE** **1 POINT**
One of Europe's longest bridges, bridges, it takes about
        7 minutes to drive across.

☐ **CHRIST THE KING STATUE** **1 POINT**
Christ looks down and protects Lisbon.

AROUND LISBON

AS A SPECIAL AGENT, YOU MUST NEVER LET YOUR GUARD DOWN. AS YOU VENTURE AROUND THE CITY, SEE HOW MANY OF THESE YOU SPOT.

☐ **AQUEDUCT** **1** POINT

When you spot this aqueduct (it carried water to the city from 1748 to 1967), check out how much Lisbon has changed from this painting.

☐ **LISBON'S CATHEDRAL** **1** POINT

(the oldest and most important church in Lisbon)

☐ **ROSSIO TRAIN STATION**

Together with your case officer (and some help from either a Portuguese person or Google Translate), figure out how to say "station" in Portuguese.

☐ **WRITE IT BELOW.**

— — — — **—** — —

CLUE 11

Be sure the right letter is on the **darker line.** You'll use this info in "Break the Code" on p.50.

☐ **SANTA JUSTA LIFT**

Have you noticed how many hills are around Lisbon? Here stands one way city residents could avoid the climb. Now, this spot is a tourist attraction with nice views at the top.

PENA PALACE

AERIAL VIEW

ENTRANCE

To arrive at Pena Palace entrance today you probably had to do some hiking. If you had come about 170 years ago (when most of this was built), maybe you would've arrived in your carriage, excited to attend an important event at this colorful palace. (See the bright red and yellow towers?) However, after you hopped out of your carriage, you took a closer look at the entrance arch, and maybe wondered if the king and queen actually wanted you to come inside.

☐ FIND THESE TWO TYPES OF CREATURES "WELCOMING" YOU TO THE PALACE. (1 POINT EACH, 5 POINTS MAX)

LIONS   SNAKES

1
POINT
EACH

MERMAN / TRITON

SHELL

If these creatures didn't get you excited to party with the royal family, maybe this guy would.

VENTURE THROUGH THE ARCH, UP THE HILL, TO THE TERRACE, AND FIND:

☐ **THE MERMAN** **1 POINT**

The Merman (also called a "triton," a sea-god) looks pretty upset to be stuck holding the stone window upon his back. Legend has it that a merman appeared on nearby beach around 500 years ago.

☐ **3 HUGE SHELLS BY THE MERMAN** **1 POINT**

As you explore more of the palace, stay alert for one more large shell.

Hint: It's somewhere in this part.

Venture to the cloister (courtyard). Once there:

☐ **WHAT ANIMALS SUPPORT THE LARGE SHELL?** **1 POINT**

CLOISTER / COURTYARD

```
sketch space (see below):
```

Been to the Jeronimos Monastery (Mission #1) yet?
This place was also built for monks who followed
the teachings of St. Jerome (like the monastery
in Mission #1). (Sadly, much of the monk's
monastery was destroyed by the earthquake of 1755
(p.20), but this part remains.

Time to track down some sculptures in the
courtyard.

#1

☐ ONE POINT EACH FOR #1 & #2

1 POINT EACH

☐ ONE POINT EACH FOR SIMILAR
ONES YOU FIND (7 POINTS MAX)

1 POINT EACH

#2

☐ CLOSELY EXAMINE THE SCULPTURES
TO FIND YOUR FAVORITE. THEN,
SKETCH IT ABOVE AND GIVE HIM/HER
A UNIQUE NAME.
(You can do this later in the day
if you run out of time here.)

3 POINTS

Earlier, you found shell sculptures, now it's
time to track down some real shells.

☐ FIND A COLLECTION OF REAL SHELLS.

2 POINTS

(Hint: The shells decorate the walls of a
lower-level room, just off the courtyard,
inside a door shaped like this.).............

FERDINAND

AMÉLIE

CARLOS

MANUEL

As you explore inside, remain on the lookout for pictures of Portugal's royals who called this palace home.

☐ **ONE POINT FOR EACH ROYAL PICTURE (5 POINTS MAX)**

1 POINT EACH

(The images you find may not appear exactly like these.)

Manuel was Portugal's last king. For around 800 years kings and queens ruled the country. However, by the early 1900's, many Portuguese were fed up with the royals.

Manuel, fearing for his life, fled. He hopped in a boat just up the coast, and lived the rest of his life in England.

MANUEL'S ESCAPE

The next time you have to dress up for a photo - don't complain. How would you like to wear velvet, lace, and stockings like Manuel had to?

CAMERA: WILL LOOK
SIMILAR (BUT NOT
EXACTLY THE SAME)

TELEPHONE

As you make your way through the palace, how many
of these "high-tech" objects can you spot from
the mid 1800s/early 1900s?

☐ CAMERA 1 POINT

☐ TELEPHONE 1 POINT

☐ OLD-FASHIONED TOILET (THAT FLUSHES) 1 POINT

Something we take for granted today, but back
then, this was a big deal!

☐ HOT SHOWER 1 POINT

Another thing that we appreciate only when it's
gone - a hot shower. Back then, only the richest
families had these.

☐ ON THE UPPER LEVEL OF THE
PALACE, LOCATE THE CHAPEL 2 POINTS
ENTRANCE.

Venture inside and...

☐ **FIND THIS BUILDING INSIDE THE CHAPEL.**

A model of the monastery that stood here around 500 years ago - before lightning damage and the 1755 earthquake.

☐ **FIND A GREEN FEATHER NEARBY.**

Pena (as in Pena Palace) = feather

Time for a pop quiz!

☐ 1. **FIND THE IMAGE OF BELEM TOWER.**

☐ 2. **WHO'S THIS KNIGHT? (HINT: HE JUST SLAYED A DRAGON.)**

Need help? Look through the Lisbon missions.

The palace has incredible views up the coast and also to the Moorish Castle. And on a clear day, your view goes all the way to Lisbon.

☐ **WHAT INTERESTING THINGS ARE THERE TO SEE TODAY?**

MOORISH CASTLE

SPECIAL AGENTS MUST BE IN TIP-TOP SHAPE. MAKE IT ALL THE WAY TO THE TOP OF THIS PLACE, AND YOU'VE PASSED THE FITNESS PART OF THE SPECIAL AGENT TEST.

☐ FIND "SINTRA" WRITTEN IN ARABIC ON A FLAG.

1 POINT

Arabic = the language of the Moors, the people who built this fortress around 1100 years ago.

my notes:

THE MOORS

☐ SPOT PENA PALACE. **1** POINT

☐ LOCATE THE NATIONAL PALACE. **1** POINT

Geography quiz time – for your case officer.

☐ ASK YOUR CASE OFFICER IF THE WATER YOU SEE IS THE: **1** POINT

  A. MEDITERRANEAN SEA
  B. ATLANTIC OCEAN
  C. GULF OF CÁDIZ ("CAH-DEEZ")

Ask your case officer to check the answer at the end of the book and report back to you!

NATIONAL PALACE

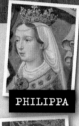

PHILIPPA

JOHN

Portugal's royal family had palaces throughout the country, and before you stands their home in Sintra. They lived here on and off from the 1400's to 1800's. Wondering what those pointed structures are? Chimneys. (More on those later.) Hope you like birds - it's time to track some down inside and rack up points!

☐ **SWANS: 1 POINT EACH, 5 MAX**   **1 POINT EACH**

Swans were a family symbol of Queen Philippa, who ruled Portugal when most of this palace was built.

☐ **MAGPIES: 1 POINT EACH, 5 MAX**   **1 POINT EACH**

Magpies have a reputation for making lots of noise. The story goes that Philippa's husband (King John) gave a kiss to another lady. This made palace workers gossip like magpies. King John had these painted to remind the workers not to gossip.

☐ **DOVES: 1 POINT EACH, 5 MAX** `1 POINT EACH`

Hint: Find these in the palace chapel. They symbolize the Holy Spirit.

As you can tell from this book, ships are very important in Portugal's history.

TRACK DOWN THESE VESSELS (ALL IN THE SAME ROOM):

☐ **PORTUGUESE SHIP** `1 POINT`

☐ **OTTOMAN EMPIRE SHIP** `1 POINT`

☐ **BONUS: FIND A SHIP** `2 POINTS` **WITH THE FLAG BELOW.**

PORTUGUESE SHIP

NETHERLANDS FLAG

OTTOMAN EMPIRE SHIP

Portuguese_eyes / Vítor Oliveira

COAT OF ARMS ROOM

MANUEL

☐ **TRACK DOWN THE COAT-OF-ARMS ROOM.** **2 POINTS**

    A coat-of-arms is like a symbol (or group of symbols) of a family. Back in the 1500's, King Manuel had this room decorated with the coats-of-arms of the royal family and the 72 most important families in Portugal. (Imagine the disappointment of finding out you were the 73rd most important family in Portugal!)

☐ **FIND MANUEL'S COAT-OF-ARMS (THE FANCIEST, OF COURSE).** **1 POINT**

See the smaller deer around the room? Check out all the things the deer manage to do at once: balance objects on their heads, wave flags from their antlers, and have crests wrapped around their necks (the families' coats of arms).

family coat-of-arms space (see below):

Closely examine the families' coats-of-arms in the room.

☐ IF YOU HAD TO PICK ONE FOR YOUR FAMILY, WHICH ONE WOULD YOU CHOOSE AND WHY? **2** POINTS

Imagine you had to create a totally new coat-of-arms for your family, complete with different objects symbolizing your family.

☐ DRAW IT ABOVE. **3** POINTS

☐ BEFORE LEAVING THE PALACE, LOCATE THE KITCHEN. **2** POINTS

☐ HAVE A LOOK UP ONE OF THE MASSIVE CHIMNEYS YOU SAW FROM OUTSIDE. **1** POINT

VIEW UP CHIMNEY

QUINTA DA REGALEIRA

("Keen-tah Dah Reg-ah-leh-rah")

Quinta: a mansion with lots of land

Regaleira: the woman who first owned this had the title "Countess of Regaleira"

This mansion once belonged to a man who got rich selling coffee and gems. And way more interesting than this - he possibly belonged to a **secret society** (a secret group). We don't know this for sure, of course. (As a member of a secret society, you must keep your membership secret!) Either way, this place is filled with all kinds of mysterious spots.

Wander around the gardens and locate:

☐ AN UNDERGROUND TUNNEL (TWO POINTS EACH, FOUR POINTS MAX)

2 POINTS EACH

my notes:

_____

_____

_____

☐ **A WATERFALL** **2 POINTS**

☐ **THE "INITIATION WELL"** **2 POINTS**

(Not a real well, but a spiral staircase that some say was used for **secret ceremonies** for new members of the secret society.)

Secret societies sometimes have secret handshakes so that members can tell if someone actually belongs to the group or not. When it's time for a break from sightseeing...

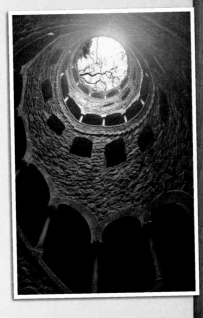

☐ **COME UP WITH YOUR OWN SECRET HANDSHAKE FOR YOUR TEAM.** **3 POINTS**

Teach it to your team members, and then it's time for a test.

☐ **TEST YOUR TEAMMATES TO SEE IF THEY CAN REMEMBER THE SECRET HANDSHAKE.** **3 POINTS**

ANYTIME MISSIONS

THE BEST AGENTS HAVE A HIGH LEVEL OF SOMETHING CALLED "SITUATIONAL AWARENESS." THESE QUICK-WITTED AGENTS PAY CLOSE ATTENTION TO THEIR SURROUNDINGS — READY TO COLLECT CRITICAL INTEL. HAVING EXCELLENT SITUATIONAL AWARENESS ("SA" FOR SHORT) MEANS ALWAYS BEING "ON ALERT."

These missions will test your SA. You can complete these at any time during your stay. Don't let your guard down as you wander around town, or you may miss a chance to win points.

TRANSPORTATION

How many can you spot?

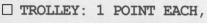 ☐ TROLLEY: 1 POINT EACH, 10 POINTS MAX

1 POINT EACH

☐ TUK TUK: 1 POINT EACH, 10 POINTS MAX

1 POINT EACH

(Each must be a different color or have a different logo.)

☐ CARGO SHIP: 1 POINT EACH, 10 POINTS MAX

1 POINT EACH

SPORTING

BENFICA

SOCCER (ALSO CALLED FOOTBALL)

In Portugal, soccer (football) is serious business, and you must pick a side! **Sporting vs. Benfica.** (Benfica = "Ben-fee-kuh")

Benfica Symbol: Eagle

Sporting Symbol: Lion

If you can't decide, then together with your case officer, ask some advice from a Portuguese person (a tour guide, a restaurant server, etc.). Once you choose, no switching is allowed, so choose wisely! Once you've made your decision...

☐ **FIND YOUR TEAM'S EQUIPMENT (JERSEY, SCARF, FLAG, ETC.) 1 PT FOR EACH TYPE, 10 PTS MAX**

1 POINT EACH

☐ **SPEAKING OF SOCCER/FOOTBALL, LOCATE A JERSEY FOR PORTUGAL'S NATIONAL TEAM.**

1 POINT

The colors may be different, but look for the Portuguese cross (circled in this pic).

PORTUGAL'S RONALDO

CARAVEL

"FADO" (PORTUGAL'S TRADITIONAL MUSIC)

PAINTED TILES

Called an "azulejo" ("*ah-zoo-lay-jo*"), these hand-painted tiles can be kind of like a painting - but on tile. (See pics above.)

☐ **LOCATE A DESIGN WITH AT LEAST THREE COLORS. 1 POINT EACH, 10 POINTS MAX**

 1 POINT EACH

☐ **FIND A PAINTING OF AN EVENT, PERSON, OR PLACE (NOT JUST A DESIGN). 1 POINT EACH, 10 POINTS MAX**

 1 POINT EACH

☐ **FIND AN AZULEJO OF A SIGHT FROM ONE OF YOUR MISSIONS. 3 POINTS EACH, 12 POINTS MAX**

3 POINTS EACH

☐ **BONUS: WHAT IS THE NAME OF THE SIGHT IN THE AZULEJO YOU FOUND?**

2 POINTS

TILE PAINTING WITH JERONIMOS MONASTERY (MISSION #1)

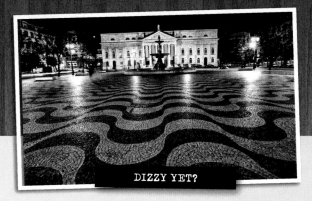

DIZZY YET?

COBBLESTONE DESIGNS

Strolling along the city streets, keep a look out below your feet.

☐ FIND UNIQUE DESIGNS LIKE WAVES, DIAMONDS, AND
  MORE AT CITY PLAZAS AND ON SIDEWALKS.
  1 POINT FOR EACH PLAZA/SIDEWALK, 10 POINTS MAX

1
POINT
EACH

Hint: Above is Rossio Square, around the corner from the Rossio station (p.27).

AMALIA
(FAMOUS PORTUGUESE
FADO SINGER)

SARDINES ANYONE?

SARDINE STORE

SEAFOOD

Much of Portugal borders the sea, so seafood is super-important here.

☐ **TRY BACALHAU** **1 POINT**

"Bah-kah-yow" ("yow" as in "cow"). Bacalhau = cod. According to Portuguese chefs, you can cook bacalhau 365 ways - one for each day of the year.

FRIED BACALHAU

☐ **BUY A CAN OF SARDINES.** **2 POINTS**

Know anyone back home who loves seafood? Bring this to them as a souvenir. These cans can be quite fancy, and some Lisbon shops specialize in canned sardines. Just make sure to pack your souvenir carefully - you definitely wouldn't want sardine oil leaking into your luggage!

DESSERT TIME

☐ **TRY PASTEL DE NATA** **1 POINT**

"Pah-sh-tell duh Nah-tah"
We saved the best food, a custard tart, for last.

PASTEL DE NATA

PORTUGUESE "SPHERE"

Earn tons up points by locating this Portuguese symbol all over the place at monuments, on flags, signs, tiles, doorways, the list goes on and on.

Long before GPS, Portugal's sailors used this tool to help find the way across the ocean blue. It came to symbolize Portugal's exploration around the globe.

☐ 1 POINT EACH, 20 POINTS MAX

1 point for each *kind* of sphere. (For example, once you find it on a Portuguese flag, that's it for points for finding it on the Portuguese flag.)

GOOD LUCK ROOSTER

☐ 1 POINT FOR EACH DIFFERENT KIND OF GOOD LUCK ROOSTER SPOTTED, 10 POINTS MAX

And when you're on your mission, try not to walk backwards – that's considered bad luck in Portugal.

But, if you forget and end up walking backwards, no worries. You can reverse your bad luck by *accidentally* wearing your clothes backwards. That's considered good luck in Portugal!

STREET ART

Not your usual messy spray paint graffiti;
the creators of this street art had
permission to decorate buildings with
these designs above and below.

NO

☐ 2 PTS PER STREET ART MURAL, 20 PTS MAX

2 POINTS EACH

Moral of the one below: be considerate, especially
when using a selfie stick!

ANYTIME MISSIONS: BONUS

COME ACROSS A PLACE THAT'S CLOSED? NOT
ENOUGH TIME IN LISBON / SINTRA? HAVE NO
FEAR, USE THESE MISSIONS TO ACHIEVE YOUR
GOAL. YOUR CASE OFFICER SETS THE POINTS.

SPEAKING PORTUGUESE:

Time to put your language skills to the test!
Below you'll find some situations to test your
Portuguese.

Earn points each time you say one of these phrases
to a different Portuguese person.

☐ **SAY HELLO** (for example, to staff at your hotel)

"OLÁ" (*"Oh-lah"*)

POINT(S)
EACH

☐ **SAY THANK YOU** (for example, to a server)

"OBRIGADA" - GIRLS SAY THIS (*"Oh-bree-gah-dah"*)

POINT(S)
EACH

"OBRIGADO" - BOYS SAY THIS (*"Oh-bree-gah-doh"*)

☐ **SAY GOODBYE** (for example, to staff at your hotel)

"ADEUS" (*"Ah-day-oosh"*)

POINT(S)
EACH

BREAK THE CODE

Ready for your most challenging mission yet? Save this one for last. Have you noticed the **clue labels** scattered throughout the book?

The below Portuguese message is missing letters. Use the clue labels to break the code and complete this important message for agents.

> Example: Clue #1 is on p.8. The letter you would have written for Clue #1 on p.8 is "C". So, write "C" for the Clue #1 label below.

(If you couldn't fill in all the clue labels, your case officer may help you break the code using the Answer Key.)

QUEM VÊ

5
POINTS

CARAS ___ ___ ___

| CLUE 7 | CLUE 3 | CLUE 4 |

VÊ

C ___ ___ ___ ___ ___ ___ ___

| CLUE 1 | CLUE 5 | CLUE 8 | CLUE 9 | CLUE 11 | CLUE 2 | CLUE 6 | CLUE 10 |

Filled in all the missing letters? This is pronounced something like: *"Kayn Vay Car-ahsh Now Vay Core-ah-soy-sh"*. And translated in English, it means something like, "Those who see faces do not see hearts."

A similar saying to this:
Don't judge a book by its cover.

Remember this important lesson while operating as a special agent: don't trust appearances - things may not be what they seem.

If you broke this code and earned the needed points, then congratulations! You've proven you have what it takes to be a SIA special agent.

Fill out the below to make it official. (Use your special agent name, of course.)

SIA SPECIAL AGENT ANNOUNCEMENT

This document certifies that

_____
write your special agent name here

has successfully completed a series of challenging missions to officially become a special agent with the SIA.

_____
case officer's signature   *date*

p.7: The explorer: Vasco da Gama

p.8: The poet's last name: Camões

p.10: 3 things missing in painting: skull in window sill, hourglass in window sill, white feather in ink;

      A male lion in Portuguese: leão ("lay-ow")

p.13: Mary holds grapes.

p.15: Henry holds a ship.

p.17: The 2 letters: P and O.

p.20: The missing animal: elephant.

p.24: The street: Rua Augusta.

p.27: Station in Portuguese is: estação ("esh-tah-sow")

p.29: Turtles support the shell.

p.33: The knight is St. George

p.35: The water is the Atlantic Ocean.

p.50: The message: Quem vê caras não vê corações

Case officers may check answers here. Many clues do not have only one right answer. For those that do, here are they are.

ANSWER KEY   CASE OFFICERS ONLY

THE FINAL MISSION

"I'm Entering Today!"

☐ Case officers: Take a clever pic of your MISSION book in Portugal (or back at home) & enter our photo contest for a chance at bragging rights & an Amazon giftcard!

Check out our website for more info:
ScavengerHuntAdventures.com/Contest

PLEASE HELP SPREAD THE WORD

"We'd Love To Help!"

We're a small family business and would be thrilled if you recommended our books to a family member or friend.

Our books: Paris, London, Amsterdam, Rome, NYC, D.C., Barcelona, Florence, St. Augustine, with more coming!

THANK YOU

Thank you for supporting our family business. Mom writes, Dad serves in the military, Grandma is VP of Logistics, and Jr. helps research our books.

Without readers this wouldn't be possible.
Thank <u>YOU</u>!

Catherine

Made in United States
Orlando, FL
17 May 2022